SIN ON WHEELS

PRISMATIC
PUBLICATIONS
LOS ANGELES

Cover image in public domain
Quotes by the incomparable Mae West

Copyright ©2017
Prismatic Publications
All rights reserved
ISBN 978-1-943986-47-7
Printed in in USA

www.JournalsOnAmazon.com

*I'LL TRY ANYTHING ONCE, TWICE IF I
LIKE IT, THREE TIMES TO MAKE SURE*

I USED TO BE SNOW WHITE,
BUT I DRIFTED

TOO MUCH OF A GOOD THING
CAN BE WONDERFUL

*I'VE BEEN IN MORE LAPS
THAN A NAPKIN*

I GENERALLY AVOID TEMPTATION
UNLESS I CAN'T RESIST IT

TO ERR IS HUMAN,
BUT IT FEELS DIVINE

THE BEST WAY TO BEHAVE
IS TO MISBEHAVE

I LIKE RESTRAINT, IF IT
DOESN'T GO TOO FAR

ANYTHING WORTH DOING
IS WORTH DOING SLOWLY

THOSE WHO ARE EASILY SHOCKED
SHOULD BE SHOCKED MORE OFTEN

I'M NO ANGEL, BUT I'VE
SPREAD MY WINGS A BIT

I'M A GOOD WOMAN
FOR A BAD MAN

Collect Them All!

www.JournalsOnAmazon.com

Made in the USA
San Bernardino, CA
03 October 2018